Time for a Checkup

By Janice Behrens

ISBN: 978-1-338-88868-3

Editor: Liza Charlesworth
Art Director: Tannaz Fassihi; Designer: Tanya Chernyak
Photos ©: 7: LightField Studios/Shutterstock.com; 8: Rawpixel.com/Shutterstock.com.
All other photos © Getty Images.

1 2 3 4 5 6 7 8 9 10   68   31 30 29 28 27 26 25 24 23
Printed in Jiaxing, China. First printing, January 2023.

SCHOLASTIC INC.

How is your heart?
Let's check it and see.
Your heart sounds good to me.

How is your nose?
Let's check it and see.
Your nose looks good to me.

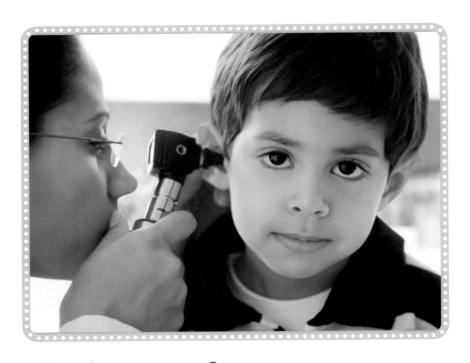

How is your ear?
Let's check it and see.
Your ear looks good to me.

How is your eye?
Let's check it and see.
Your eye looks good to me.

How is your mouth?
Let's check it and see.
Your mouth looks good to me.

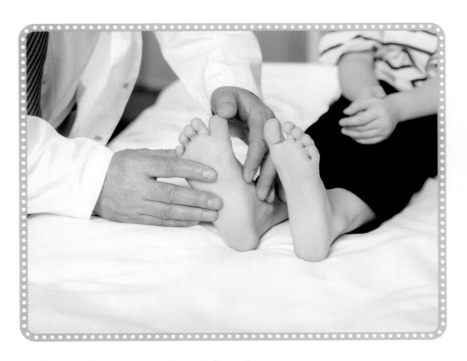

How is your foot?
Let's check it and see.
Your foot looks good to me.

How is your bear?
Let's check it and see.
Your bear looks good to me!